Fish Tales

Joe Brown

DEDICATION

This book is dedicated to my Son Andrew. He has always been my fishing partner and an incredible part of my life. Nothing is more enjoyable than a day on the water with him catching fish, surviving storms, sharing adventures and doing life together.

ACKNOWLEDGMENTS

This book wouldn't have been possible if not for all of my family and friends who spend time fishing with me, building relationship and basically making life an incredible experience.

Men and women perceive size differently, especially when describing the fish that got away.

"Somebody behind you while you are fishing is as bad as someone looking over your shoulder while you write a letter to your girl." - Ernest Hemingway

"Do not tell fish stories where the people know you... but particularly, don't tell them where they know the fish."
- Mark Twain

"Here's the deal, throw me back and I won't text your boss telling him you called in sick to fish."

Q: What kind of music do fishermen listen to?
A: Something catchy!

Q: What do you get when you cross a fishing lure with a dirty sock?
A: A hook, line and stinker!

Q: Why won't Batman fish with Robin anymore?
A: Because Robin ate all the worms!

"Carpe Diem" does not mean "fish of the day."
-Author Unknown

"He may look small but he put up a heck of a fight."

"I hate the first day of fishing season."

Jesus was banned from all future fishing tournaments.

Two fishermen are fishing in a boat under a bridge. One looks up and sees a funeral procession starting across the bridge. He stands up, takes off his cap, and bows his head. The procession crosses the bridge and the man puts on his cap, picks up his rod and reel, and continues fishing.

The other guy says, "That was touching. I didn't know you had it in you."

The first guy responds, "Well, I guess it was the thing to do - after all, I was married to her for 40 years

"Most of the world is covered by water. A fisherman's job is simple:
Pick out the best parts."
-Charles Waterman

"Oh that's a missionary school."

No one in this town could catch any fish except this one man. The game warden asked him how he did it. The man told the game warden that he would take him fishing the next day. Once they got to the middle of the lake the man took out a stick of dynamite, lit it, and threw it in the water. After the explosion fish started floating to the top of the water. The man took out a net and started picking up the fish. The game warden told him that this was illegal. The man took out another stick of dynamite and lit it. He then handed it to the game warden and said " are you going to fish or talk".

"Fly fishermen are born honest, but they get over it."
- Ed Zern

Jesus always enjoyed a day on the water fishing.

"Look at where Jesus went to pick people. He didn't go to the colleges… he got guys off the fishing docks." - Jeff Foxworthy

"Let's not tell anyone about this spot."

"You bet I had it mounted, it gave me the best fight of my life."

"Just confirming, there are no catch limits or size restrictions?"

"So, do you fish for sport or do you actually catch something?"

Bob is sitting on the ice all day fishing with no luck, not even a nibble. Cold and tired he is about to leave, when a guy walks up cuts a hole in the ice beside him, and starts pulling out fish as fast a he can drop his hook in the water. Bob can't believe it, he yells over" what's your secret?" "wogaatakakeptemwrm" he answers back. "what did you say?" replies Bob. The man spits a large ball of worms on the ice and says to Bob," you have to keep your worms warm".

"There are only two occasions when Americans respect privacy, especially in Presidents. Those are prayer and fishing."
-Herbert Hoover

"OK kids, I'll tell the story one more time..."

Hank's pull rope snaps on a hard start.

"Just reach under his belly and lift him into the boat."

"You might want to let that one go..."

"Fishing is much more than fish. It is the great occasion when we may return to the fine simplicity of our forefathers." – Herbert Hoover

"If people concentrated on the really important things in life, there'd be a shortage of fishing poles." – Doug Larson

"Many men go fishing all of their lives without knowing that it is not fish they are after" – Henry David Thoreau

A man was stopped by a game warden recently with two buckets of fish leaving a lake known for its fishing. The game warden asked the man, "Do you have a license to catch those fish?"

The man replied; "No, sir. These are my pet fish."

"Pet fish?" the warden replied.

"Yes, sir. Every night I take these here fish down to the lake and let them swim around for a while. I whistle and they jump back into their buckets, and I take them home."

"That's a bunch of hooey! Fish can't do that!"

The man looked at the game warden for a moment, and then said, "Here, I'll show you. It really works."

"O.K. I've GOT to see this!" The game warden was curious now. The man poured the fish in to the lake and stood and waited. After several minutes, the game warden turned to the man and said:

"Well?" "Well, what?" the man responded.

"When are you going to call them back?" the game warden prompted.

"Call who back?" the man asked.

"The FISH." "What fish?" the man asked.

"Honestly, I was just washing my worms."

Shore fishing requires threading the needle.

"There's a fine line between fishing and standing on the shore like an idiot." – Steven Wright

"I mounted a beautiful fish and had a great meal too."

"I'll bet you have some stories."

"I caught one, I actually caught one."

Three priests were fishing on a boat when they ran out of bait. The first priest got up and walk across the water to get some more bait. After 2 hours they ran out of bait again and the second priest said he would go get more bait...so he got up and walk across the water. After 3 hours of fishing they ran out of bait again and the third priest said he would get more bait. So, he stepped out of the boat and went straight to the bottom. The first priest turned to the second priest and asked, "Should we have told him where the rocks were?

"Record or not, throw it back."

"By my count, that is the 27th last cast."

Fishermen dread the spot where lures hang heavy from the trees like spanish moss.

One day a rather inebriated ice fisherman drilled a hole in the ice and peered into the hole and a loud voice said, "There are no fish down there."

He walked several yards away and drilled another hole and peered into the hole and again the voice said, "There's no fish down there."

He then walked about 50 yards away and drilled another hole and again the voice said, "There's no fish down there."

He looked up into the sky and asked, "God, is that you?"

"No, you idiot," the voice said, "it's the rink manager."

"Be patient and calm, for no one can catch fish in anger."
- Herbert Hoover

Two fishermen travel 100 miles to try out a new fishing spot. They buy a variety of bait and lures and rent a boat. After a long day of fishing, the two fishermen return to the dock. The first fisherman pulls their only catch from the live well, a scrawny bass just legal size. He says, "Boy! This fish cost us about $75." The second fisherman says, "Well it's a good thing we didn't catch any more."

George went fishing, but at the end of the day he had not caught one fish. On the way back to camp, he stopped at a fish store. I want to buy three trout, he said to the owner. But instead of putting them in a bag, throw them to me. Why should I do that? the owner asked. So, I can tell everyone that I caught three fish!

"It has always been my private conviction that any man who pits his intelligence against a fish and loses has it coming."
- John Steinbeck

"I'm not sure that's a keeper."

A lesson on the dangers of being online.

Paddling upstream to save a $1.79 lure snagged on a log.

"Wow, fishing sure is fun. I can't believe I caught such a big fish my first time out."

"Oh, I would say it was at least twice that size, and it had fangs and horns too..."

Simon Peter saith unto them, I go a fishing. They say unto him, we also go with thee. They went forth, and entered into a ship immediately; and that night they caught nothing.
John 21:3 (Holy Bible)

A hazard of river baptisms.

"You better have a good excuse for being late."

"I'm not sure about the new guy."

"Keep going Hank, you almost have it."

"It's obvious Jesus accepts everyone. His disciples were fishermen, and we know what kind of lies we tell."

"Settle down boy, they're not actual cat-fish."

"Frank I said I'm sorry about breaking your line. But it sure was a big fish, wasn't it."

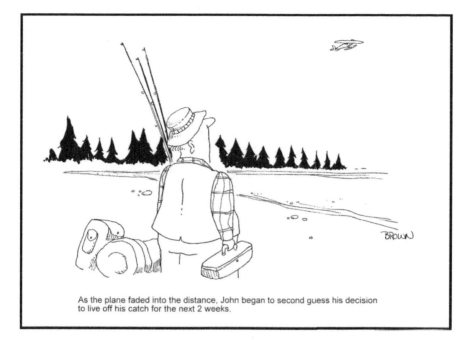

As the plane faded into the distance, John began to second guess his decision to live off his catch for the next 2 weeks.

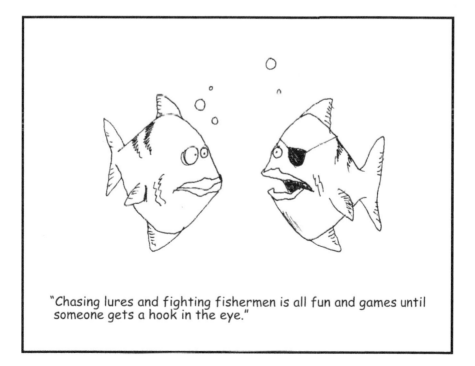

"Chasing lures and fighting fishermen is all fun and games until someone gets a hook in the eye."

"Maybe next time you won't drink so much lake water."

"For crying out loud Frank, spit it out."

"Now that's a bird nest."

"Come on Frank. I didn't mean to catch a bigger fish than you."

"Fishing is a delusion entirely surrounded by liars in old clothes."
- Don Marquis

"It is not a fish until it is on the bank."
-Author Unknown

"It's a jamming device for fish finders."

"Only caught one, eh."

ABOUT THE AUTHOR

Joe Brown is an avid fisherman and published cartoonist represented by Cartoonstock.com and has a previous book <u>Christians Laugh Too</u>, which is a collection of church related cartoons. During most of the year he can be found heading out to fish, fishing, or returning from fishing. His favorite fish is the smallmouth bass, the hardest fighter in the river. Joe's real job is at a nonprofit helping people with barriers in life find employment, other than that he is a husband, dad, and grandpa.

Printed in Great Britain
by Amazon

71356149R00031